Who Can Swim?

by Miriam Sklar

ISBN: 978-1-338-75090-4
Illustrated by John Lund

Published by Scholastic Inc., 557 Broadway, New York, NY 10012

10 9 8 7 6 5 4 68 25 26 27/0

Printed in Jiaxing, China. First printing, January 2021.

A seal can swim.

A penguin can swim.

A fish can swim.

A polar bear can swim.

A duck can swim.

A whale can swim.

I can swim!